My teeny-weeny fairy nose,
Is as pretty as a rose.

I'm a queen, all dressed in red,
A golden crown upon my head.

Giddy-up horsey, one, two, three,
Is there a rosette just for me?

Every cool pop idol needs
Star-shaped shades and groovy beads

I'm an angel, flying high,
Soaring in the moonlit sky.

Sneezing, wheezing, coughing too?
I'm here to help if you've got flu.

I like to swim and sit on rocks,
And comb my lovely flowing locks.

Ballet dancing keeps me busy,
But twirling round makes me dizzy.

I love to wear a bright pink top,
When I dance to disco pop.

A beautiful bride I may be,
But can you find a ring for me?

I'm a witch who likes to wear,
Bats and spiders in my hair.

Find a sparkly mask disguise,
For my pretty princess eyes.